CREATION
JOURNAL

_____

NAME

_____

YEAR

ISBN: 978-0-9844021-9-9
Editing by Kathy West
Cover & layout by Timothy Kavmark

Live Your Truth Press
support@liveyourtruth.com
liveyourtruth.com

"We are creating each day. If you take the time each night to write out what you want to experience the next day, you will consistently have the best days of your life. Life can be consistently remarkable for you if you take the time to create it."

Remembering Wholeness
Carol Tuttle

YOU ARE THE CREATOR OF YOUR LIFE.

Whether you are intentional about creating your life or not, your beliefs, thoughts, and feelings broadcast a vibration that comes back into your life multiplied. If you want to know what your deeper beliefs are, look at your life and it will tell you. If you believe you need to worry or complain, you will attract a lot of people and experiences to worry and complain about.

The good news is that you can shape your beliefs, thoughts, and feelings, so that you can attract into your life people and experiences that support your highest good.

This Creation Journal guides you through a key process I use to intentionally create my life, day by day.

Every night before I go to sleep, I take time to write the experience I want to create the following day. No matter how tired I am, I always take the time to write out my intentions. I saw the benefits of this process play out in the year 2020. In a year where most people survived, I thrived. I ended the year healthier, happier, and wealthier as a result of this practice of consciously creating my life day by day. I want that for you!

Bless You,
Carol Tuttle

HOW TO USE THIS CREATION JOURNAL

This journal works differently from other journals.

In other journals, you look back at the past to make a record of it. In this journal, you look forward to create the future.

As I teach in my book, Remembering Wholeness, the process of creation is a simple five-step process. Understanding this process, and practicing it to gain mastery, allows us to become master creators.

The Five-step Process of Creation:

1. *Know what you want.*

2. *Ask for what you want.*

3. *Believe you can have it.*

4. *Let go and allow.*

5. *Express gratitude when you receive it.*

On the following pages, you'll see how this journal helps you to apply this five-step process to create the best days of your life.

STEP ONE: KNOW WHAT YOU WANT.

In order to create what you want, you have to know what it is. Writing about it the night before helps you to do that. For example, on Sunday night, write your intentions for Monday in the space for Monday. Continue that way throughout the week. You are writing what you want to experience before it happens.

STEP TWO: ASK FOR WHAT YOU WANT.

By writing down your intention, you are asking a power greater than yourself to assist you in creating it. When I started using this process, I wrote my own intentions in present tense, as if I were experiencing them in real time. I now write them in past tense, as if they have already come to pass—trusting that they will. Look to the instructions and examples on the following pages to guide you.

STEP THREE: BELIEVE YOU CAN HAVE IT.

As you focus your attention on what you want to create, the energy responds. One way to lift your level of belief and focus your attention is by energy sketching—actually drawing out your creations and intentions. Look to the instructions and examples on the following pages to guide you.

STEP FOUR: LET GO AND ALLOW.

In other words, get out of your own way and don't try to force it. Your only job is to follow through on inspired action. Don't stress about whether or not your creation will manifest itself. Be patient and consistent. This Creation Journal is a practice, not a one-time event. As you stick with it, you are seeding a powerful energy to consciously manifest a life of joy.

STEP FIVE: EXPRESS GRATITUDE WHEN YOU RECEIVE IT.

Gratitude actually starts the cycle all over. It is the completion and the beginning of the creation process. Gratitude energy initiates more things manifesting in your life for which you feel gratitude. The creation process is one eternal round.

When practiced with humility, this process can only bring you more of what you want, by visualizing the energy of what you want to create into your life, starting the day before. The more you trust this process, the more you will experience what you write.

HOW TO WRITE YOUR OWN INTENTIONS & AFFIRMATIONS

An intention is a statement that you write or speak to focus your mental, emotional, and energetic vibration to support the creation process. The simple acts of changing your thoughts and articulating your desires create different outcomes in your life.

Intentions generally begin with the phrase "I am..." and are followed by the experience you want to experience. But the wording can be variable for what supports you.

As you write in your journal the night before, begin your intentions for the following day with gratitude and trust.

For example:

- *I am grateful for...*

- *I am grateful that...*

- *I love experiencing...*

At the beginning of each month, write down your intentions in the monthly calendar pages. Each evening, create your life day by day by writing in the weekly pages.

Here are examples from my personal Creation Journal to give you some ideas. You can write in general terms:

"What wants to happen, happens. What wants to show up, shows up. Where the energy goes, I go. Everything that occurs today is for my highest and greatest good. I am blessed."

Or you can get specific about important events or dates. Notice that I write my intentions as having already occurred:

"I am grateful I woke up fully refreshed and ready to create a great day. I really enjoyed being home and getting ready for our 'I Love My Life' virtual event. Today exceeded my expectations. I loved it."

Take a moment to practice writing an intention here. Writing something simple that you want to experience tomorrow:

Once you set your intention, let go of trying to make it happen, and follow your intuition to take inspired action.

HOW TO DO ENERGY SKETCHING

This is a simple but powerful creation technique done by drawing a visual representation of your intention with a pen or pencil.

Manifesting your intentions is the process of bringing your idea into the physical world. By crafting your intention by the physical act of drawing, you make the energy of your written intention even more potent. The visual, physical reference you draw evokes an energy that is put into motion to manifest what you drew. Just by the nature of the activity, Energy Sketching focuses your energy on your intention longer because it requires you to take some time representing what you want.

To create your own energy sketches, you do not need to be a good artist. You can draw stick figures and your sketch can be simplistic or messy. In fact, do not focus on drawing "realistically" unless you want to.

Focus on drawing a picture or symbol that represents the intention and future you want to create.

SOME EXAMPLES...

If you feel stuck or adrift in your life, and you want to get yourself back on the right path for you, draw an actual path. Add sketches of what you want to experience on that path, such as happy family members or dollar signs. You can even add written words or intentions to your sketch.

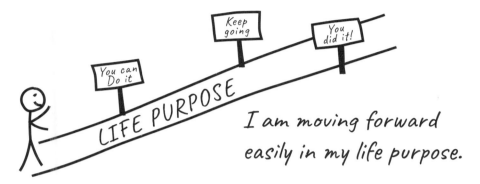

If you are feeling disconnected from someone important to you, draw an energy sketch of connection and love. For example, you can draw the two of you as stick figures and then sketch figure 8s between you, connecting you.

To see a full gallery of energy sketch examples, visit

caroltuttle.com/energysketch

EXAMPLE MONTH

At the beginning of each month, take a moment to create your experience for the upcoming weeks. Write your intentions in present or past tense, as if they have already happened.

Note dates that are important to you in this month that you want to create. Add any sketches or affirmations you feel inspired to include.

MONTH _May_

MONDAY	TUESDAY	WEDNESDAY	THURSDAY	FRIDAY	SATURDAY	SUNDAY
	1	2	3 *My festive birthday*	4	5	6
7	8	9	10	11	12	13 *A relaxing Mother's Day*
14	15	16	17	18 *I finished my project*	19	20
21	22 *My fun trip*	23	24	25	26	27
28	29	30	31			

Write an intention for specific dates and what you want to create on those days.

IMPORTANT DATES

DATE	WHAT I WANT TO CREATE
3 May	*I am grateful that my birthday felt celebratory and festive.*
7 May	*I loved how my Mother's Day was full of rest and good food.*
18 May	*I'm grateful that I easily completed my big project.*
22-27 May	*My trip was fun and adventurous and the weather was perfect!*

EXAMPLE MONTH

Choose a word that you want to experience this month. This exercise can be a practice in choosing a fun theme or a supportive guide for what you want to create.

WORD OF THE MONTH

Remarkable 💭

MY INTENTION(S) FOR THIS MONTH

May is going to be a fantastic month. I am grateful I have the motivation I need to accomplish the more important items in my life right now. Even when I am my busiest, I am going to remember to take the time to to notice the changing seasons: the new leaves on the trees, the blue sky, and the beautiful flowers that are blooming everywhere. I am grateful that my money continues to grow in flow and accumulation. I am creating an excess of money this month. I am taking care of myself both emotionally and physically. I am motivated to eat healthy and work out. I am also grateful that all of my relationships are better than ever.

What do you want to experience all month long? Write your intentions or do some energy sketching here.

GRATITUDE FOR THE MONTH I JUST ENDED

May was a wonderful month. I am grateful for the new experiences I had. I especially loved trying out all the new healthy recipes I cooked. We had a great time visiting our family and as I had hoped, we got along beautifully. Thank you May for all the lovely experiences and growth I enjoyed.

At the end of the month, come back here to express gratitude for what manifested. This starts the process of creation over again.

EXAMPLE WEEK

Each evening, write your intentions for the following day. For example,
on Sunday night, write Monday's intentions in Monday's space.

DATE *May 14-20*

MONDAY — I wake up, I get up, I show up! I feel rested after a great night's sleep. My meetings are superb. My life is wonderful. I am grateful for being me! I am grateful for my body.

TUESDAY — I am grateful that the results of my hair appointment are going even better than I had hoped for. My stylist listened to what I wanted and interpreted as I had hoped. I love my hair! 5 stars for a great new hairstyle.

WEDNESDAY — I am grateful that everyone I work with at my job is easy to get along with and always motivated to give their best effort. The project we are working on is coming together beautifully. I love my job.

THURSDAY — I am knowing how to grow my income of money and how to create more accumulation. I am attracting the correct people to help me do this. My meetings today went exceptionally well.

FRIDAY — Feeling strong, confident, and healthy today. I enjoyed lunch with some friends and it was just enough time together. We all left feeling grateful and renewed. Be Patient. Be Kind. Be Loveable. Be Present. Be Observant.

SATURDAY — What wants to happen today happens. What I am meant to tune into I receive inspiration for. I am motivated to use my time for what is the most timely and important today. I trust my intuition to guide me.

SUNDAY — It was a beautiful day to rest and catch up on things around the house. I took time to nurture myself and take care of myself. I even enjoyed watching a movie that I wanted to see and I really loved it. Such a beautiful day.

EXAMPLE WEEK

Dinners for this week:
- Quesadillas, salad
- Split pea soup
- Pizza, salad
- Chicken wings, potato casserole, asparagus
- Stir fry with rice

To-do's:
- Returns
- Set up oil change
- Order groceries
- Mend pants
- Paint
- Order tickets
- Research new cars

Mtgs = Great Outcomes

WORK MEETING

ME

NEW CAR

I am attracting the perfect car
at a price that works for me!
I love my new car!

Healing Center Journaling:
Healing Plan for Lack of Self-Confidence

I have believed a confident person is... someone who speaks their truth.

The traits I admire in myself are... willing to laugh at myself, good teacher, disciplined, take on challenges, friendly, accepting.

NOW IT'S YOUR TURN

You've read the instructions. You've seen the examples. Now, you get to practice creating your life, day by day.

This journal has three sections to support you:

- *1 big-picture creation page for the year.*

- *12 monthly creation spreads. After this page, you'll find twelve month-long intention sections right in a row. Come back to this section at the beginning of every month.*

- *52 weekly creation spreads. Follow the simple process outlined in this journal and you will create your amazing life in the year to come.*

You are a powerful creator.

How amazing can your life look next year?

It's time to find out.

WORD OF THE YEAR

MY INTENTIONS FOR THIS YEAR

_____
_____
_____
_____
_____
_____
_____
_____
_____
_____
_____
_____
_____
_____
_____
_____
_____
_____
_____
_____
_____
_____
_____
_____
_____
_____
_____
_____
_____
_____
_____
_____
_____

MONTH _____

MONDAY	TUESDAY	WEDNESDAY	THURSDAY	FRIDAY	SATURDAY	SUNDAY
○	○	○	○	○	○	○
○	○	○	○	○	○	○
○	○	○	○	○	○	○
○	○	○	○	○	○	○
○	○	○	○	○	○	○

IMPORTANT DATES

DATE   WHAT I WANT TO CREATE

_____   _____

_____   _____

_____   _____

_____   _____

_____   _____

*"Energy follows thought and what you focus
on, you create faster than ever. Start with
your thoughts in the present moment."*

MY INTENTION(S) FOR THIS MONTH

GRATITUDE FOR THE MONTH I JUST ENDED

MONTH _____

MONDAY	TUESDAY	WEDNESDAY	THURSDAY	FRIDAY	SATURDAY	SUNDAY

IMPORTANT DATES

DATE   WHAT I WANT TO CREATE

_____   _____

_____   _____

_____   _____

_____   _____

_____   _____

"Oftentimes, change needs to start with re-writing our own script from one of self-shaming and criticism to one of self-love and admiration."

MY INTENTION(S) FOR THIS MONTH

GRATITUDE FOR THE MONTH I JUST ENDED

MONTH _____

MONDAY	**TUE**SDAY	**WED**NESDAY	**THURS**DAY	**FRI**DAY	**SAT**URDAY	**SUN**DAY

IMPORTANT DATES

DATE   WHAT I WANT TO CREATE

_____   _____

_____   _____

_____   _____

_____   _____

_____   _____

*"Take ownership of your thinking mind. Train
your mind to do what you want it to do in
order to create the reality you want."*

MY INTENTION(S) FOR THIS MONTH

GRATITUDE FOR THE MONTH I JUST ENDED

MONTH _____

MONDAY	TUESDAY	WEDNESDAY	THURSDAY	FRIDAY	SATURDAY	SUNDAY

IMPORTANT DATES

DATE   WHAT I WANT TO CREATE

_____   _____

_____   _____

_____   _____

_____   _____

_____   _____

"Now is a powerful time to claim what is true for you and to trust in what you can create, regardless of what you've been through previously."

MY INTENTION(S) FOR THIS MONTH

GRATITUDE FOR THE MONTH I JUST ENDED

MONTH _____

MONDAY	TUESDAY	WEDNESDAY	THURSDAY	FRIDAY	SATURDAY	SUNDAY
○	○	○	○	○	○	○
○	○	○	○	○	○	○
○	○	○	○	○	○	○
○	○	○	○	○	○	○
○	○	○	○	○	○	○

IMPORTANT DATES

DATE	WHAT I WANT TO CREATE
_____	_____
_____	_____
_____	_____
_____	_____
_____	_____

"When we see ourselves as limiting and lacking, we take from the world. When we see ourselves as affluent and abundant, we share real love with the world."

MY INTENTION(S) FOR THIS MONTH

GRATITUDE FOR THE MONTH I JUST ENDED

MONTH _____

MONDAY	TUESDAY	WEDNESDAY	THURSDAY	FRIDAY	SATURDAY	SUNDAY
○	○	○	○	○	○	○
○	○	○	○	○	○	○
○	○	○	○	○	○	○
○	○	○	○	○	○	○
○	○	○	○	○	○	○

IMPORTANT DATES

DATE   WHAT I WANT TO CREATE

_____ _____

_____ _____

_____ _____

_____ _____

_____ _____

"As long as you can stay clear, balanced, and grounded,
you become the most powerful person in any experience
to shift the energy from negative to positive."

MY INTENTION(S) FOR THIS MONTH

GRATITUDE FOR THE MONTH I JUST ENDED

MONTH _____

MONDAY	TUESDAY	WEDNESDAY	THURSDAY	FRIDAY	SATURDAY	SUNDAY

IMPORTANT DATES

DATE   WHAT I WANT TO CREATE

_____   _____

_____   _____

_____   _____

_____   _____

_____   _____

"Take 15 minutes every day to go within and connect
with your inner voice and knowing. If you don't have
15 minutes because you are too busy, take an hour!"

MY INTENTION(S) FOR THIS MONTH

GRATITUDE FOR THE MONTH I JUST ENDED

MONTH _____

MONDAY	TUESDAY	WEDNESDAY	THURSDAY	FRIDAY	SATURDAY	SUNDAY
◯	◯	◯	◯	◯	◯	◯
◯	◯	◯	◯	◯	◯	◯
◯	◯	◯	◯	◯	◯	◯
◯	◯	◯	◯	◯	◯	◯
◯	◯	◯	◯	◯	◯	◯

IMPORTANT DATES

DATE	WHAT I WANT TO CREATE
_____	_____
_____	_____
_____	_____
_____	_____
_____	_____

*"Remembering our wholeness is a
lifelong journey and what we came
to this planet to experience."*

MY INTENTION(S) FOR THIS MONTH

GRATITUDE FOR THE MONTH I JUST ENDED

MONTH _____

MONDAY	TUESDAY	WEDNESDAY	THURSDAY	FRIDAY	SATURDAY	SUNDAY
○	○	○	○	○	○	○
○	○	○	○	○	○	○
○	○	○	○	○	○	○
○	○	○	○	○	○	○
○	○	○	○	○	○	○

IMPORTANT DATES

DATE	WHAT I WANT TO CREATE
_____	_____
_____	_____
_____	_____
_____	_____
_____	_____

*"We live at a time when healing can happen even
more quickly than ever before on this planet. Tap into
the energetic imbalance, release it, and heal."*

WORD OF THE MONTH

MY INTENTION(S) FOR THIS MONTH

GRATITUDE FOR THE MONTH I JUST ENDED

MONTH _____

MONDAY	TUESDAY	WEDNESDAY	THURSDAY	FRIDAY	SATURDAY	SUNDAY

IMPORTANT DATES

DATE   WHAT I WANT TO CREATE

_____   _____

_____   _____

_____   _____

_____   _____

_____   _____

*"Use the powerful intuitive and spiritual gifts
you have been endowed with to make your life
better first. Then use them to bless others."*

WORD OF THE MONTH

MY INTENTION(S) FOR THIS MONTH

GRATITUDE FOR THE MONTH I JUST ENDED

MONTH _____

MONDAY	TUESDAY	WEDNESDAY	THURSDAY	FRIDAY	SATURDAY	SUNDAY
◯	◯	◯	◯	◯	◯	◯
◯	◯	◯	◯	◯	◯	◯
◯	◯	◯	◯	◯	◯	◯
◯	◯	◯	◯	◯	◯	◯
◯	◯	◯	◯	◯	◯	◯

IMPORTANT DATES

DATE	WHAT I WANT TO CREATE
_____	_____
_____	_____
_____	_____
_____	_____
_____	_____

_"As a result of seeing your world through
a gratitude lens, you can only attract
more of which to be grateful for."_

MY INTENTION(S) FOR THIS MONTH

GRATITUDE FOR THE MONTH I JUST ENDED

MONTH _____

MONDAY	TUESDAY	WEDNESDAY	THURSDAY	FRIDAY	SATURDAY	SUNDAY

IMPORTANT DATES

DATE   WHAT I WANT TO CREATE

_____   _____

_____   _____

_____   _____

_____   _____

_____   _____

"Look for things to be joyful about, pray for the gift of joy to be granted to you, tap into the energy of joy that children so effortlessly live in."

WORD OF THE MONTH

MY INTENTION(S) FOR THIS MONTH

GRATITUDE FOR THE MONTH I JUST ENDED

DATE _____

MONDAY

TUESDAY

WEDNESDAY

THURSDAY

FRIDAY

SATURDAY

SUNDAY

DATE _____

MONDAY

TUESDAY

WEDNESDAY

THURSDAY

FRIDAY

SATURDAY

SUNDAY

DATE _____

MONDAY

TUESDAY

WEDNESDAY

THURSDAY

FRIDAY

SATURDAY

SUNDAY

DATE _____

MONDAY

TUESDAY

WEDNESDAY

THURSDAY

FRIDAY

SATURDAY

SUNDAY

DATE _____

MONDAY

TUESDAY

WEDNESDAY

THURSDAY

FRIDAY

SATURDAY

SUNDAY

DATE _____

MONDAY _____
_____
_____
_____
_____

TUESDAY _____
_____
_____
_____
_____

WEDNESDAY _____
_____
_____
_____
_____

THURSDAY _____
_____
_____
_____
_____

FRIDAY _____
_____
_____
_____
_____

SATURDAY _____
_____
_____
_____

SUNDAY _____
_____
_____
_____
_____

DATE _____

MONDAY

TUESDAY

WEDNESDAY

THURSDAY

FRIDAY

SATURDAY

SUNDAY

DATE _____

MONDAY

TUESDAY

WEDNESDAY

THURSDAY

FRIDAY

SATURDAY

SUNDAY

DATE _____

MONDAY

TUESDAY

WEDNESDAY

THURSDAY

FRIDAY

SATURDAY

SUNDAY

NOTES / JOURNALING / ENERGY SKETCHING

DATE _____

MONDAY

TUESDAY

WEDNESDAY

THURSDAY

FRIDAY

SATURDAY

SUNDAY

DATE _____

MONDAY

_____
_____
_____
_____

TUESDAY

_____
_____
_____
_____

WEDNESDAY

_____
_____
_____
_____

THURSDAY

_____
_____
_____
_____

FRIDAY

_____
_____
_____
_____

SATURDAY

_____
_____
_____
_____

SUNDAY

_____
_____
_____
_____

DATE _____

MONDAY _____
_____
_____
_____

TUESDAY _____
_____
_____
_____

WEDNESDAY _____
_____
_____
_____

THURSDAY _____
_____
_____
_____

FRIDAY _____
_____
_____
_____

SATURDAY _____
_____
_____
_____

SUNDAY _____
_____
_____
_____

DATE _____

MONDAY _____

_____

_____

_____

_____

TUESDAY _____

_____

_____

_____

_____

WEDNESDAY _____

_____

_____

_____

_____

THURSDAY _____

_____

_____

_____

_____

FRIDAY _____

_____

_____

_____

_____

SATURDAY _____

_____

_____

_____

_____

SUNDAY _____

_____

_____

_____

_____

DATE _____

MONDAY _____

TUESDAY _____

WEDNESDAY _____

THURSDAY _____

FRIDAY _____

SATURDAY _____

SUNDAY _____

DATE _____

MONDAY

_____
_____
_____
_____

TUESDAY

_____
_____
_____
_____

WEDNESDAY

_____
_____
_____
_____

THURSDAY

_____
_____
_____
_____

FRIDAY

_____
_____
_____
_____

SATURDAY

_____
_____
_____
_____

SUNDAY

_____
_____
_____
_____

DATE _____

MONDAY

_____
_____
_____
_____

TUESDAY

_____
_____
_____
_____

WEDNESDAY

_____
_____
_____
_____

THURSDAY

_____
_____
_____
_____

FRIDAY

_____
_____
_____
_____

SATURDAY

_____
_____
_____
_____

SUNDAY

_____
_____
_____
_____

DATE _____

MONDAY

TUESDAY

WEDNESDAY

THURSDAY

FRIDAY

SATURDAY

SUNDAY

DATE _____

MONDAY

_____
_____
_____
_____

TUESDAY

_____
_____
_____
_____

WEDNESDAY

_____
_____
_____
_____

THURSDAY

_____
_____
_____
_____

FRIDAY

_____
_____
_____
_____

SATURDAY

_____
_____
_____
_____

SUNDAY

_____
_____
_____
_____

DATE _____

MONDAY

TUESDAY

WEDNESDAY

THURSDAY

FRIDAY

SATURDAY

SUNDAY

DATE _____

MONDAY _____
_____
_____
_____

TUESDAY _____
_____
_____
_____

WEDNESDAY _____
_____
_____
_____

THURSDAY _____
_____
_____
_____

FRIDAY _____
_____
_____
_____

SATURDAY _____
_____
_____
_____

SUNDAY _____
_____
_____
_____

DATE _____

MONDAY

_____
_____
_____
_____

TUESDAY

_____
_____
_____
_____

WEDNESDAY

_____
_____
_____
_____

THURSDAY

_____
_____
_____
_____

FRIDAY

_____
_____
_____

SATURDAY

_____
_____
_____

SUNDAY

_____
_____
_____
_____

DATE _____

MONDAY

TUESDAY

WEDNESDAY

THURSDAY

FRIDAY

SATURDAY

SUNDAY

DATE _____

MONDAY _____

_____

_____

_____

TUESDAY _____

_____

_____

_____

WEDNESDAY _____

_____

_____

_____

THURSDAY _____

_____

_____

_____

FRIDAY _____

_____

_____

_____

SATURDAY _____

_____

_____

_____

SUNDAY _____

_____

_____

_____

DATE _____

MONDAY

TUESDAY

WEDNESDAY

THURSDAY

FRIDAY

SATURDAY

SUNDAY

DATE _____

MONDAY

_____
_____
_____
_____

TUESDAY

_____
_____
_____
_____

WEDNESDAY

_____
_____
_____
_____

THURSDAY

_____
_____
_____
_____

FRIDAY

_____
_____
_____
_____

SATURDAY

_____
_____
_____

SUNDAY

_____
_____
_____
_____

DATE _____

MONDAY

TUESDAY

WEDNESDAY

THURSDAY

FRIDAY

SATURDAY

SUNDAY

NOTES / JOURNALING / ENERGY SKETCHING

DATE _____

MONDAY _____
_____
_____
_____
_____

TUESDAY _____
_____
_____
_____
_____

WEDNESDAY _____
_____
_____
_____
_____

THURSDAY _____
_____
_____
_____
_____

FRIDAY _____
_____
_____
_____
_____

SATURDAY _____
_____
_____
_____
_____

SUNDAY _____
_____
_____
_____
_____

DATE _____

MONDAY _____
_____
_____
_____

TUESDAY _____
_____
_____
_____
_____

WEDNESDAY _____
_____
_____
_____

THURSDAY _____
_____
_____
_____

FRIDAY _____
_____
_____
_____

SATURDAY _____
_____
_____
_____

SUNDAY _____
_____
_____
_____
_____

DATE _____

MONDAY _____

TUESDAY _____

WEDNESDAY _____

THURSDAY _____

FRIDAY _____

SATURDAY _____

SUNDAY _____

DATE _____

MONDAY _____
_____
_____
_____
_____

TUESDAY _____
_____
_____
_____
_____

WEDNESDAY _____
_____
_____
_____
_____

THURSDAY _____
_____
_____
_____
_____

FRIDAY _____
_____
_____
_____
_____

SATURDAY _____
_____
_____
_____
_____

SUNDAY _____
_____
_____
_____
_____

DATE _____

MONDAY

TUESDAY

WEDNESDAY

THURSDAY

FRIDAY

SATURDAY

SUNDAY

DATE _____

MONDAY _____

_____

_____

_____

_____

TUESDAY _____

_____

_____

_____

_____

WEDNESDAY _____

_____

_____

_____

_____

THURSDAY _____

_____

_____

_____

_____

FRIDAY _____

_____

_____

_____

_____

SATURDAY _____

_____

_____

_____

_____

SUNDAY _____

_____

_____

_____

_____

DATE

MONDAY

TUESDAY

WEDNESDAY

THURSDAY

FRIDAY

SATURDAY

SUNDAY

DATE _____

MONDAY

TUESDAY

WEDNESDAY

THURSDAY

FRIDAY

SATURDAY

SUNDAY

DATE _____

MONDAY

TUESDAY

WEDNESDAY

THURSDAY

FRIDAY

SATURDAY

SUNDAY

DATE _____

MONDAY

TUESDAY

WEDNESDAY

THURSDAY

FRIDAY

SATURDAY

SUNDAY

DATE _____

MONDAY

TUESDAY

WEDNESDAY

THURSDAY

FRIDAY

SATURDAY

SUNDAY

DATE _____

MONDAY

TUESDAY

WEDNESDAY

THURSDAY

FRIDAY

SATURDAY

SUNDAY

DATE _____

MONDAY

TUESDAY

WEDNESDAY

THURSDAY

FRIDAY

SATURDAY

SUNDAY

DATE _____

MONDAY _____
_____
_____
_____

TUESDAY _____
_____
_____
_____

WEDNESDAY _____
_____
_____
_____

THURSDAY _____
_____
_____
_____

FRIDAY _____
_____
_____
_____

SATURDAY _____
_____
_____
_____

SUNDAY _____
_____
_____
_____

DATE _____

MONDAY

_____
_____
_____
_____

TUESDAY

_____
_____
_____
_____

WEDNESDAY

_____
_____
_____
_____

THURSDAY

_____
_____
_____
_____

FRIDAY

_____
_____
_____
_____

SATURDAY

_____
_____
_____
_____

SUNDAY

_____
_____
_____
_____

MONDAY

TUESDAY

WEDNESDAY

THURSDAY

FRIDAY

SATURDAY

SUNDAY

DATE _____

MONDAY _____
_____
_____
_____

TUESDAY _____
_____
_____
_____
_____

WEDNESDAY _____
_____
_____
_____

THURSDAY _____
_____
_____
_____

FRIDAY _____
_____
_____
_____

SATURDAY _____
_____
_____
_____

SUNDAY _____
_____
_____
_____
_____

DATE _____

MONDAY

TUESDAY

WEDNESDAY

THURSDAY

FRIDAY

SATURDAY

SUNDAY

DATE _____

MONDAY _____
_____
_____
_____
_____

TUESDAY _____
_____
_____
_____
_____

WEDNESDAY _____
_____
_____
_____
_____

THURSDAY _____
_____
_____
_____
_____

FRIDAY _____
_____
_____
_____
_____

SATURDAY _____
_____
_____
_____
_____

SUNDAY _____
_____
_____
_____
_____

DATE _____

MONDAY

_____
_____
_____
_____

TUESDAY

_____
_____
_____
_____

WEDNESDAY

_____
_____
_____
_____

THURSDAY

_____
_____
_____
_____

FRIDAY

_____
_____
_____
_____

SATURDAY

_____
_____
_____
_____

SUNDAY

_____
_____
_____
_____

DATE _____

MONDAY _____
_____
_____
_____
_____

TUESDAY _____
_____
_____
_____
_____

WEDNESDAY _____
_____
_____
_____
_____

THURSDAY _____
_____
_____
_____
_____

FRIDAY _____
_____
_____
_____

SATURDAY _____
_____
_____
_____

SUNDAY _____
_____
_____
_____
_____

DATE _____

MONDAY
_____
_____
_____
_____

TUESDAY
_____
_____
_____

WEDNESDAY
_____
_____
_____

THURSDAY
_____
_____
_____

FRIDAY
_____
_____
_____

SATURDAY
_____
_____
_____

SUNDAY
_____
_____
_____
_____

DATE _____

MONDAY

TUESDAY

WEDNESDAY

THURSDAY

FRIDAY

SATURDAY

SUNDAY

DATE _____

MONDAY

TUESDAY

WEDNESDAY

THURSDAY

FRIDAY

SATURDAY

SUNDAY

DATE _____

MONDAY

TUESDAY

WEDNESDAY

THURSDAY

FRIDAY

SATURDAY

SUNDAY

DATE _____

MONDAY

TUESDAY

WEDNESDAY

THURSDAY

FRIDAY

SATURDAY

SUNDAY

GRATITUDE FOR THE YEAR I JUST ENDED

"Love your life. Love the process of remembering your wholeness. Have fun along the way. We are eternal beings, so we never stop progressing. There is no destination, just more opportunities to create from higher levels of light."

Remembering Wholeness
Carol Tuttle

RESOURCES TO SUPPORT YOU IN CREATING YOUR LIFE

Books by Carol Tuttle

Remembering Wholeness

It's Just My Nature

The Child Whisperer

Mastering Affluence

The Modern Chakra Guide

Programs by Carol Tuttle

The Carol Tuttle Healing Center

Energy Profiling

Dressing Your Truth for Women

Dressing Your Truth for Men

The 30-Day Money Cure

Online access to Carol Tuttle's work

RememberingWholeness.com

CarolTuttle.com

HealWithCarol.com

DressingYourTruth.com

TheChildWhisperer.com